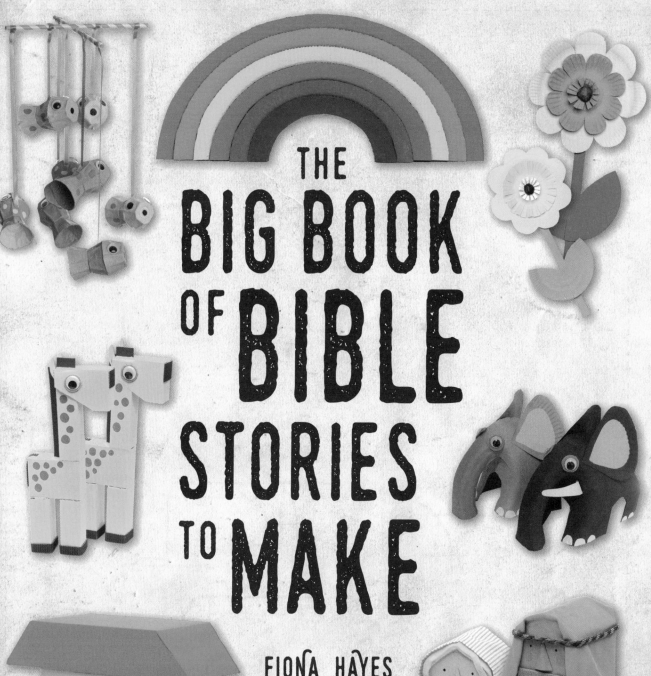

THE
BIG BOOK
OF BIBLE
STORIES
TO MAKE

FIONA HAYES

QED

Contents

Basic Equipment

Most of these projects use some or all of the following equipment, so keep these handy:

- **PVA glue**
- **Scissors**
- **Pencils**
- **Ruler**
- **Felt-tip pens**
- **Paint brushes**

These projects use a range of cardboard and plastic materials from the home, so hang on to your recycling!

Sun and Planets

In the beginning, God made the Sun and planets. Celebrate God's creation by making a universe mobile of your own!

You will need

Four large paper plates

Paints

Nine pairs of paper bowls, of varying sizes

Ten pieces of cord of varying lengths

Thick card

Nine lolly sticks

Ribbon

1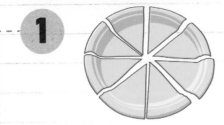

Cut a large paper plate into eight sections.

2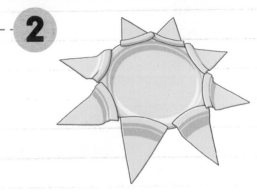

Glue the sections around the edge of another large paper plate, as shown.

3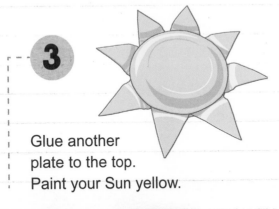

Glue another plate to the top. Paint your Sun yellow.

4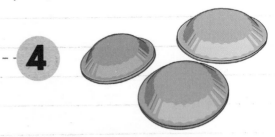

To make each planet, glue two paper bowls together. Make up eight planets of varying sizes, plus one small (or dwarf) planet for Pluto. Paint them different colours.

5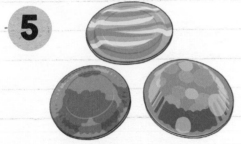

Add details, such as land and oceans, craters and swirling gases.

6

Cut away the middle from a large paper plate. Paint the rim yellow to make Saturn's rings.

7

Cut a notch on opposite sides of Saturn. Slot in the ring and glue it in place. Make a hole in the top of the Sun and planets, and tie a piece of cord to each one.

8

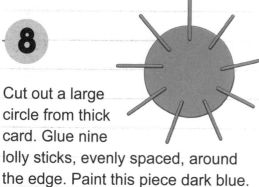

Cut out a large circle from thick card. Glue nine lolly sticks, evenly spaced, around the edge. Paint this piece dark blue.

9

Make a hole in the middle of the blue circle, thread the Sun's cord through the hole and tie a knot in the end.

10

Tie the planets to the lolly sticks. Make them hang at different heights. Glue three lengths of ribbon, evenly spaced, to the top of the blue circle. Tie the other ends together. Hang up your amazing Solar System!

Garden of Eden

Next, God made Adam and Eve to look after the world. Make the beautiful Garden of Eden, where they lived!

1

Paint a large piece of thick card green for the grass. Paint two paper bowls different greens for hills. Paint a plate blue for a pond. Glue them to the grass.

2

Paint a cardboard tube brown and a paper cup green. Glue the cup onto the tube to make a tree.

3

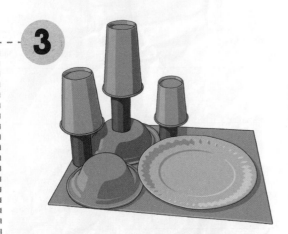

Make up two more trees using different-sized tubes and cups. Glue one on a hill and two on the grass.

4

For the apple tree, glue two paper bowls together and paint them green. Paint a short cardboard tube brown. Cut two slits in the top of the tube as shown.

5

Cut five egg box bowls from the base of an egg box.

**6**

Paint the egg box bowls bright red for apples.

7

Slot the green bowls into the slits in the tube and glue in place. Glue the apples to the tree.

8

To make flowers, cut all the bowls from two egg boxes and paint them different colours. Cut slits all around the edges of the egg box bowls.

9

Glue the apple tree and the flowers to the grass. Stick scrunched-up balls of tissue paper into the flowers and add some card leaves. It looks like paradise!

Flowers

Turn your bedroom into a Garden of Eden by filling it with these pretty flowers!

Flower one

1

To make two of these flowers, cut two large and two small paper plates into flower shapes and paint them as shown.

2

Cut two bowls from the base of an egg box.

3

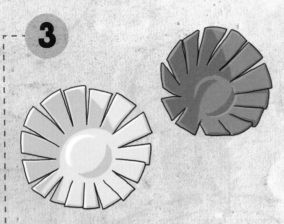

Paint the egg box bowls. Then cut slits all around the edges.

4

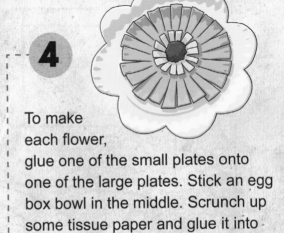

To make each flower, glue one of the small plates onto one of the large plates. Stick an egg box bowl in the middle. Scrunch up some tissue paper and glue it into the egg box bowl.

8

Flower two

5

Cut four small paper plates in half. Roll and glue them into cones. Make some wider than others.

6

Paint the outsides of the cones light pink and the insides dark pink.

Flower three

7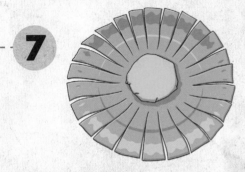

Paint a paper bowl blue. Cut slits all around the edge. Cover a jar lid with tissue paper and glue it to the centre. Repeat to make another flower.

Stems and leaves

8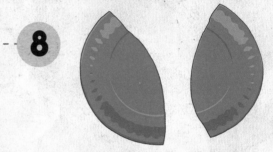

Cut eight leaf shapes from four small paper plates. Paint them green.

9

To make the stems, cut five long strips from some thick card and paint them green. Glue the flowers and leaves to the stems. Now have fun turning your bedroom into a Garden of Eden!

Fish Mobile

Make some little fishes like the ones that swam in the streams of the Garden of Eden.

You will need

Four egg boxes
Paints
Sixteen googly eyes
Two paper straws
Ribbon

1

For each fish, cut three bowls from the base of an egg box.

2 Glue the egg box bowls together to make a fish, as shown.

3

Make up seven more fish and paint them different colours. Stick a pair of googly eyes onto each fish. Draw black circles for the mouths.

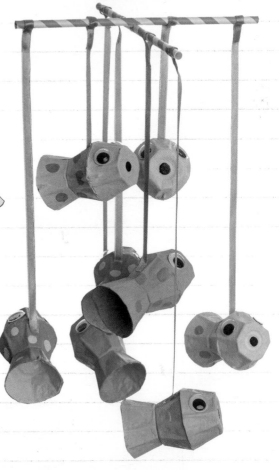

4

Gently flatten the middle of two paper straws and glue them together to make a cross.

5 Glue a length of ribbon to each fish. Attach four fish, evenly spaced, to each straw. Glue another piece of ribbon to the top of the straws so you can hang up your mobile. Now watch your little fishes swim!

Animal Finger Puppets

God brought all the animals to Adam so he could name them. What names would you give these cute little animals?

1

For each puppet, gently flatten one end of a short cardboard tube and glue the end shut. Paint the heads as shown.

2

Cut out five pairs of ears from card and paint them.

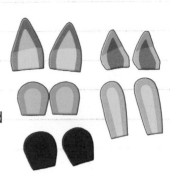

3

Glue the ears in place and bend some of them over at the top. Paint spots and stripes, as shown.

4

Glue on the googly eyes, as shown.

5

Cut out five felt noses and glue them onto the dog, panda, tiger, rabbit and pig. Draw on mouths, as shown. Give a puppet show!

11

Birds

Make a tree full of brightly coloured birds like the ones that filled the Garden of Eden.

1

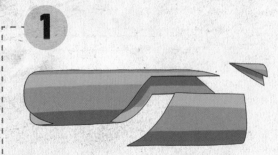

Gently flatten a long cardboard tube and cut it as shown.

2

Paint the rounded head end a lighter colour than the tail end, as shown.

3

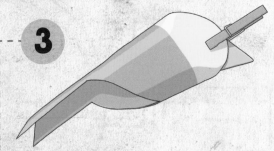

For the beak, cut a triangle from thick card and paint it yellow. Sandwich it between the head ends and glue the sides together. Use a clothes peg to hold it in place while the glue dries.

4

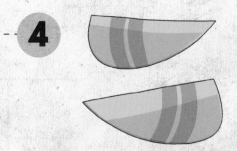

Cut out a pair of wings from thin card and paint them.

5

Glue the wings to either side of the body. Stick a pair of googly eyes onto two felt circles and glue them to the head. Cut a slit in the body below the wings, as shown.

6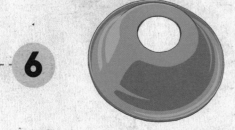

Use a pencil to make a hole for your scissors in a paper bowl. Cut out a circle the same size as the end of a cardboard tube. Paint the bowl green.

7

Cut out some branches from thick card and paint them brown.

8

Place two cardboard tubes end to end and glue a piece of thin card around the join. Paint the trunk brown. Push one end into the hole in the bowl and glue it in place. Glue the branches to the trunk. Add some leaves made from thin card.

9 Slot your bird onto a branch using the slit in its side. Make up a flock of colourful birds to sit on your tree!

Snake

A sssneaky sssnake lived in the Garden of Eden. Surprise your friends by making yours ssslither across the floor! Ssss...

1

Cut four cardboard tubes in half. Paint four pieces light green and four pieces dark green.

2

Paint a round cheese box green on the outside and pink on the inside.

3

Cut a slit on either side of the rim of the lid and fold as shown.

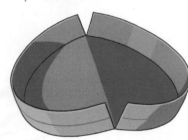

14

4

Glue half of the lid to the base. Leave the other half unglued so that the mouth opens. Glue on two bottle tops for eyes and paint them green.

5

Place the tubes and the upside-down head in a line. Glue on a length of ribbon.

Handy Hint
Always let the glue dry properly.

6

Stick two googly eyes to the bottle tops, and glue some card circles along the snake's back for spots.

7

To make the tongue, cut a strip of red card and cut a V-shape in the end. Glue it inside the snake's mouth. Ssss!

SSSS

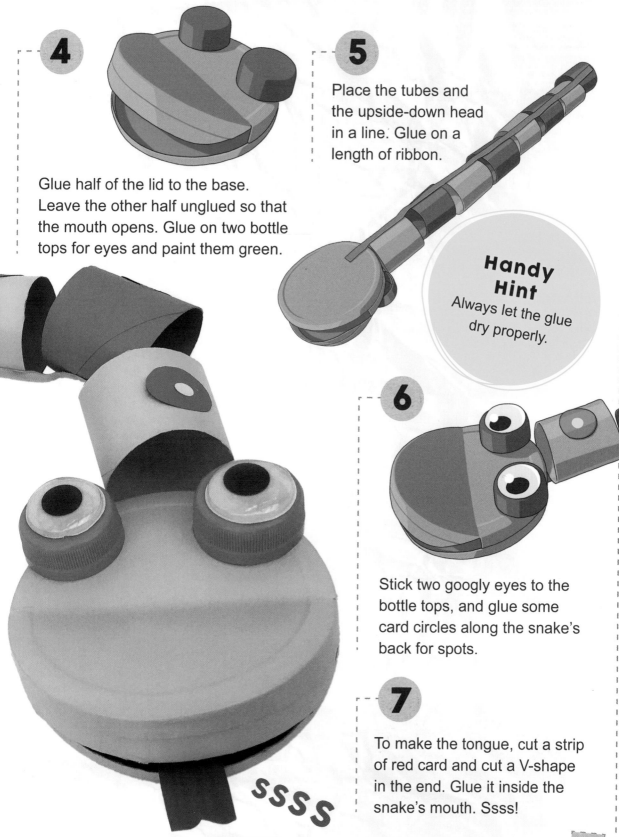

Noah and his Wife

Noah was a good man. Here he is with his wife. They're getting ready to build an ark.

You will need

Two cardboard juice cartons

Card

Paints

Ribbon

Cord

Felt

Fabric

Elastic band

1

Cut the top ridge off a tall juice carton and remove the spout. Do the same to the other carton for Noah's wife.

2

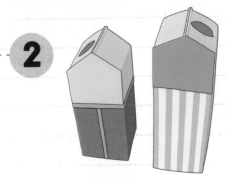

Stick some card over one side of each carton. Paint the faces and clothes. Glue some ribbon onto Noah's wife for decoration.

3

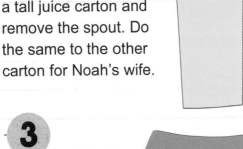

Cut out two pieces of card. The top edges will need to wrap around three sides of the cartons. Make the bottom edges slightly wider. Paint as shown.

4

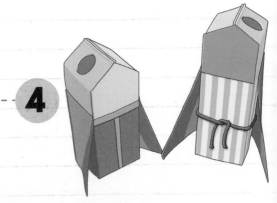

Glue the tops of the cloaks around the cartons. Gently bend the bottoms outwards. Tie some cord around Noah's middle.

5

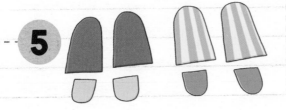

Cut out and paint two pairs of sleeves and hands.

6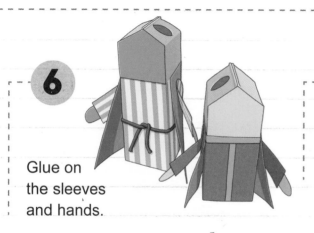

Glue on the sleeves and hands.

7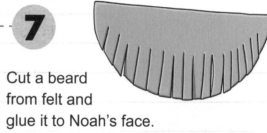

Cut a beard from felt and glue it to Noah's face.

8

Cut some strips of felt and glue them to the top and sides of Noah's wife's face.

9 Drape some fabric over Noah's head. Hold it in place with an elastic band. Glue some cord over the elastic band. Glue a scarf onto Noah's wife's head.

10

To make their noses, cut out two triangles of card and paint them. Fold them in half and glue them to the faces. Add eyes, cheeks and smiles!

The Ark

An ark is a VERY big boat. Noah built his ark and filled it with two of every kind of animal on Earth. Build an ark just like Noah's!

1

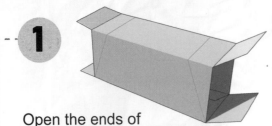

Open the ends of a long cardboard box. Cut off the side flaps. Draw two lines around the box, as shown. These are fold lines for step 2.

2

Cut a short slit along each top corner (up to the lines shown). Fold in the sides at both ends.

3

Turn the box over so the longest side is on top. Fold in the top and bottom flaps at each end and glue them to the folded-in parts. Paint this part of the ark brown.

4

Repeat steps 1 to 3 with the long, shallow box and paint it red. This is the roof.

5

Paint the rectangular cardboard box yellow for the cabin. Glue all the pieces together, as shown.

6

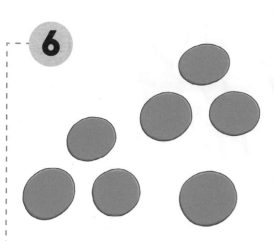

For the windows, cut seven circles from a sheet of thin, green card.

7

On a sheet of plain paper, draw seven circles slightly smaller than the windows. Draw pairs of animals inside the circles, then cut out the circles and stick them onto the card windows.

Handy Hint

Draw around cups or small jars to keep your circles nice and neat.

8

Glue the windows to the side of the ark. Noah's ark saved all the animals in the world from a mighty flood.

Penguins

Two perky penguins waddled their way onto Noah's ark.

You will need (for two penguins)

Two small plastic bottles
Black paint
White, black and yellow felt
Four googly eyes

1 Paint two small plastic bottles black.

2 Cut out two ovals of white felt. Glue them onto the bottles. These are the penguins' tummies.

3 Cut out two pairs of wings from black felt and glue them to the sides.

4 Glue a small triangle of yellow felt to their fronts for beaks.

5 Add a pair of googly eyes to your two perky penguins.

20

Elephants

Stomp, stomp! Next came two huge elephants.

1

Cut the top off a large plastic milk bottle – first ask an adult to make a hole for your scissors.

2

Cut away a dome shape from all four sides to leave legs. Cut off the bottle's top.

3

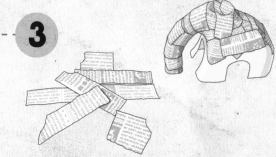

Cut some newspaper into strips. Mix up two parts PVA glue with one part water. Dip the strips into the glue and stick them all over the bottle. Make a second elephant. Paint one dark grey and the other light grey.

4

Cut a paper plate into quarters. Shape the edges to look like ears and paint them to match the bodies.

5

Glue on the ears. Stick the googly eyes onto felt circles and glue them on. Paint on some toenails and add a pair of tusks made from white card.

Giraffes

The ark must have been HUGE to fit in two tall giraffes!

You will need (for two giraffes)

Six long cardboard boxes

Four rectangular cardboard boxes

Card

Yellow and brown paint

Four googly eyes

Felt

1

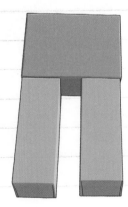

Glue two long cardboard boxes to the side of a rectangular box.

2

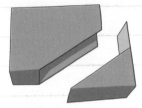

To make the head, cut the corner away from another rectangular box, as shown.

3

Glue the head to another long box, then glue this to the body.

4

Add a pair of card ears. Paint your giraffe yellow with brown spots. Use strips of brown card to add a mane, hooves, nose and tail. Make a second giraffe!

5

Stick the googly eyes onto felt circles and glue them on.

Tortoises

Two slow tortoises trundled along to join the other animals.

You will need (for two tortoises)

Two yoghurt pots

Green, yellow and brown paint

Two egg boxes

Four googly eyes

Two polystyrene balls

1 Paint two yoghurt pots different greens.

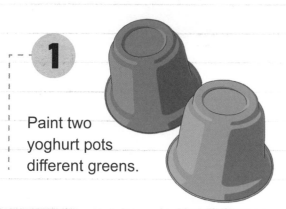

2

To make the feet, cut eight bowls from two egg boxes. Paint four of them green and four yellow.

3 Glue four feet to each pot.

4 Add spots to the shells. Paint the polystyrene balls to match the feet and glue them to the shells.

5 Add some googly eyes and mouths to these two lovable tortoises!

23

Crocodiles

1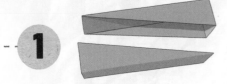

To make the tail, cut a long cardboard box in half diagonally. (Keep one piece for your second crocodile.)

2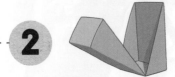

To make the head, cut a short box diagonally, keeping one side attached, as shown.

3

Take another long box and glue the head to one end. Cut the flaps off the other end and glue in the tail. Paint your croc green and pink, as shown.

4

For the legs, cut four bowls from an egg box. Paint them green and glue them to the body.

5

Cut a strip of corrugated card. Give it a wobbly top. Paint it dark green and glue it to the body.

6

Stick two long, wobbly strips of white card inside the mouth. Stick the googly eyes to two D-shaped pieces of card, as shown, and glue on. Paint spots on the body. Then make your second crocodile!

SNAP SNAP

Lions

Make these two lovable lions for Noah to take on his ark.

You will need (for two lions)

Four cardboard boxes
Yellow and pink paint
Brown paper
Four googly eyes
Thin card
Black felt

1

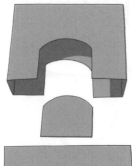

To make the body, cut the end off a cardboard box as shown.

2

Cut the corner from another box and use it for the head.

3

Cut a small corner from the other side of the box and glue it to the body for a neck.

4

Glue the head to the neck. Then paint the lion yellow.

5 Cut slits along one edge of a strip of brown paper and glue it around the neck for a mane.

6

Cut out some ears from thin card, paint as shown and glue them in place. Add a tail, a felt nose and some googly eyes, and draw on a mouth. Make a female lion with no mane.

ROAR

Parrots

Squawk! Two chatty parrots flew aboard Noah's ark. It must have been a very noisy place!

You will need (for two parrots)

Two round cheese boxes

Red, yellow, black, blue and green paint

Two long cardboard tubes

Two short cardboard tubes

Thin white card

Four googly eyes

Felt

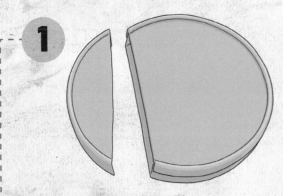

1 Cut the end off a round cheese box. Glue the lids to the bases.

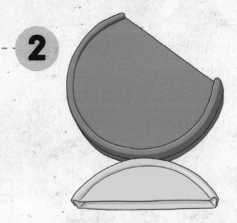

2 Paint the small piece yellow and the large piece red. Glue the small piece to the large piece, as shown.

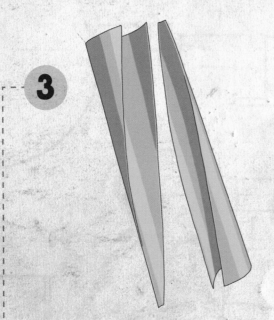

3 To make the back and tail, gently flatten a long cardboard tube. Cut it in half diagonally.

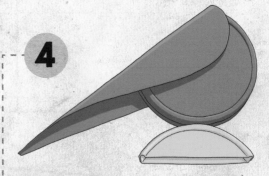

4 Round off the corners of the long tube and paint it red. Glue it to the sides of the body.

5

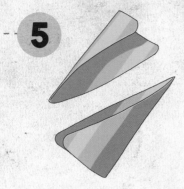

To make the head and beak, gently flatten a short cardboard tube. Cut it in half diagonally. Round off the corners.

6

Cut a slit on either side and fold as shown. Paint the head red and the beak black.

7

Fold down the sides of the beak and glue them to the inside of the head.

8

Glue the head in place.

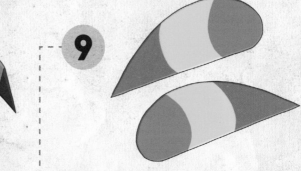

9

Cut out a pair of wings from thin card. Paint them in wide bands of colour.

10

Glue on the wings. Glue the googly eyes onto two felt circles. Stick these onto two circles of white card and glue them to the head. Now make another chatty parrot for the ark!

Dove

There was a great flood. When it stopped raining, Noah sent out a dove to look for dry land.

1

Cut two large crescent shapes from two paper plates to make the dove's body.

2

From thick card, cut two circles for the head and two triangles for the beak. Paint the beak yellow and glue the pieces between the two circles, as shown.

3

Glue the two paper plates together (except for the ridged edges). Then glue one end of the body inside the head, as shown.

4

Fold a piece of white paper into a concertina.

5

Tape one end together to make a fan. Make up two more fans.

6

Glue one fan between the crescents for a tail. Glue the other two to the body for wings. Stick the googly eyes onto two felt circles and glue them to the head. Your gentle dove is ready to leave the ark!

Rainbow

God promised never to flood the whole Earth again. To show his promise, he put a beautiful rainbow in the sky.

You will need

Thick card
Purple, blue, green, yellow, orange and red paint

1

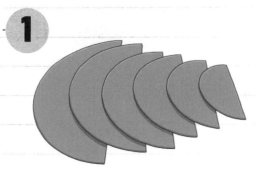

From thick card, cut out six semicircles in descending sizes.

2

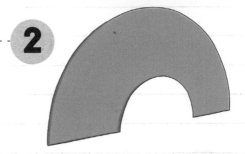

Cut out a small semicircle from the base of the largest piece.

3 Repeat using the same semicircle template for all six pieces.

4

Paint the pieces the colours of the rainbow. Glue them together in order of size and colour.

5 Your rainbow will brighten up any room and remind you of God's promise!

Joseph's Colourful Coat

Jacob gave his son Joseph a colourful coat. Make a coat for Joseph using as many colours as you can!

You will need

One cardboard canister

Paints

Cord

Card

Ribbon (lots of colours)

Brown felt

1

Paint a cardboard canister cream with a wide, skin-coloured band around the top. Tie a piece of cord around the middle.

2

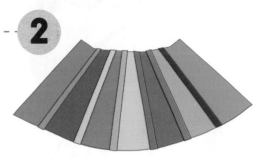

Cut out a curved piece of card – the top edge needs to wrap just over half way around the canister. Paint it with bands of colour. Glue on ribbons to make it really bright.

3

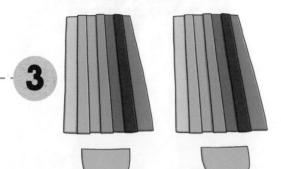

Cut out a pair of sleeves and hands. Paint them and add some ribbon for decoration.

4

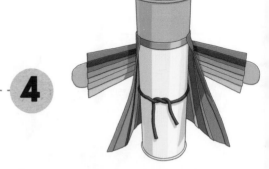

Glue the top of the coat to the canister. Gently curl the bottom edge outwards. Glue on the sleeves and hands, and stick a strip of ribbon around the neck.

5

Cut a wide strip of brown felt. Make slits all along one edge.

6

Glue the uncut edge of felt around the rim of the canister.

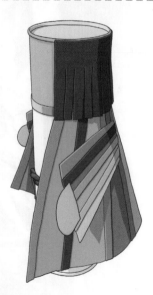

7

Cut a circle of brown felt slightly larger than the top of the canister. Cut slits all around the edge. Glue it to the top of the canister.

8

Make a nose from a small triangle of card. Paint it, fold it in half and glue it on. Add eyes, cheeks and a smile!

Handy Hint

Use scrap paper to try out lots of different colours.

Moses in a Basket

To keep her baby boy safe, Moses' mother hid Moses in a basket beside the River Nile.

You will need

One paper bowl
Light brown, dark brown and yellow paint
One paper cup
One polystyrene ball
Two pieces of fabric
Card

1 Paint a paper bowl brown. Add light and dark brown stripes around the rim.

2 Cut a paper cup in half and paint it pale yellow. Paint a polystyrene ball skin coloured and glue it to the cup.

3 Place a piece of fabric in the bowl.

4 Wrap the baby in another piece of fabric.

5 Cut out a pair of hands from card and paint them. Fold over the ends.

6 Place baby Moses in the basket. Glue his hands to the fabric and draw on a sleeping face!

Bulrushes

The king of Egypt's daughter found baby Moses hidden among some bulrushes.

You will need (for two bulrushes)

One egg box

Two long cardboard tubes

Brown and green paint

Thick card

Two paper straws

1 Cut two bowls for each bulrush from the base of an egg box.

2 Glue an egg box bowl to each end of a cardboard tube. Paint it brown.

3 Cut out some long leaf shapes from thick card and paint them green.

4 Paint a paper straw green and snip a small piece off one end. Make a hole at each end of the bulrush. Push the long piece of straw into one end and the short piece into the other end, and glue in place.

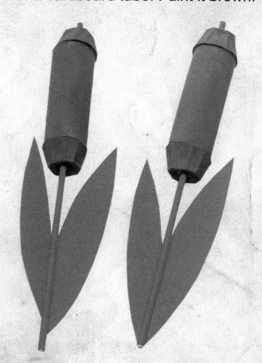

5 Glue the leaves to the stem. Make another bulrush and put them close to baby Moses!

Princess Jewellery

Make some dazzling Egyptian jewellery fit for a princess.

Necklace

1

On some card, draw a small circle inside a larger one. Cut out the circles, then cut away a piece from the narrow section of card, as shown. Paint the necklace yellow.

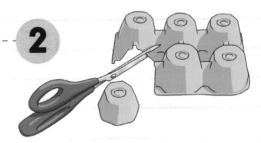

2

Cut six bowls from the base of an egg box.

3

Paint the egg box bowls bright colours. Add some white highlights.

4

Glue the jewels to the necklace.

Bracelets

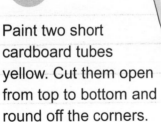

5

Paint two short cardboard tubes yellow. Cut them open from top to bottom and round off the corners.

6

Cut two bowls from an egg box. Paint as shown and glue them to the bracelets.

34

Headpiece

7

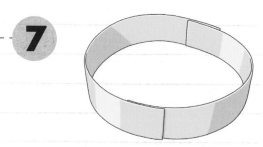

Cut a strip of card long enough to fit around your head – you may need to glue two pieces together. Glue the ends together. Paint this piece yellow.

8

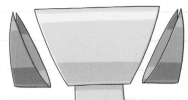

Gently flatten a short cardboard tube. Cut off the corners and glue the tube to a piece of thick card. Paint both pieces yellow.

9

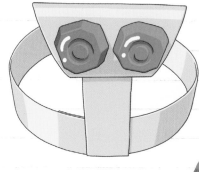

Cut another two bowls from an egg box. Paint them red and glue them to the tube to look like snake's eyes! Glue the thick card to the headband.

To finish

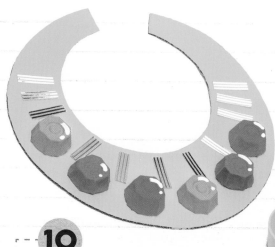

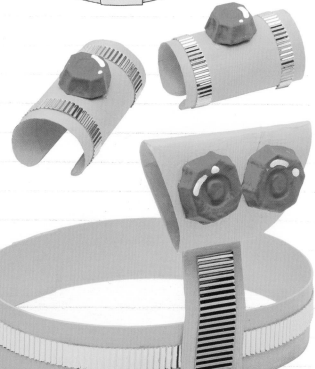

10

Cut some strips of shiny card and glue them to all the pieces. Now they are fit for a princess!

Plague of Frogs

Egypt's king would not let Moses' people pray to God. So God filled Egypt with thousands of frogs! How many frogs can you make?

You will need (for three frogs)

Three cardboard tubes

Green, pink, purple and orange paint

Card

Six googly eyes

1

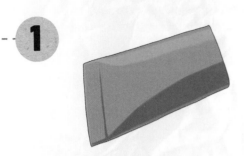

Flatten one end of a cardboard tube and glue the sides together.

2

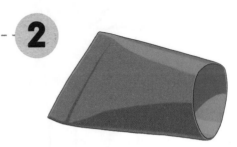

Paint the inside pink and the outside green.

3

Cut out two front legs and two thicker back legs from card. Paint the legs green.

4

Glue the legs to the underside of the body, as shown.

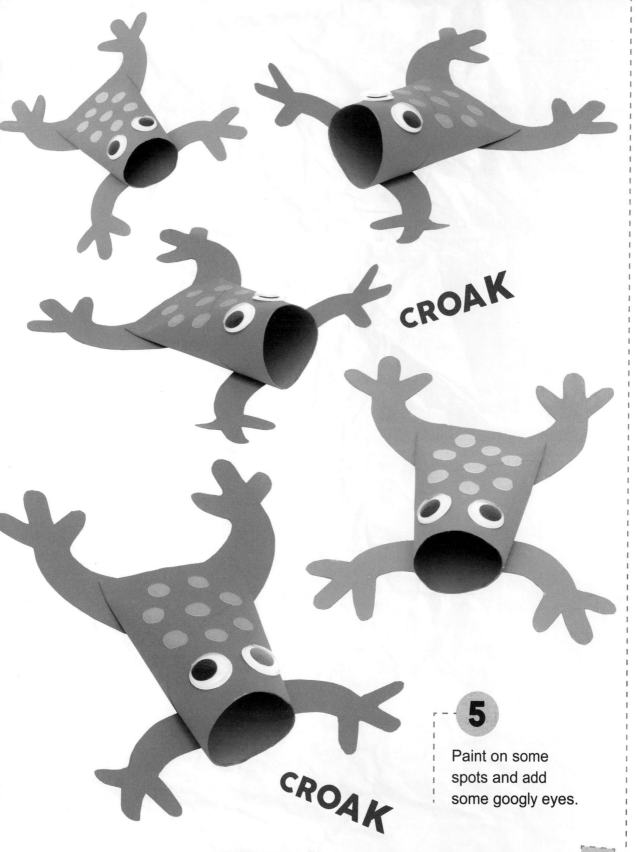

CROAK

CROAK

5

Paint on some spots and add some googly eyes.

Plague of Locusts

The king of Egypt would not let Moses' people be free. So God sent a plague of locusts to Egypt to eat up all the crops.

1

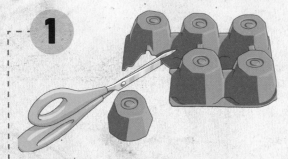

Cut three bowls for each locust from the bases of two egg boxes.

2

Cut one spike for each locust from the bases of two egg boxes.

3

Glue together the three pieces, as shown.

4

Paint the bodies in shades of green and brown.

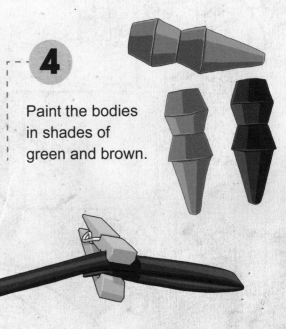

5

For the back legs, fold a paper straw into thirds. Glue one end into the middle – use a clothes peg to hold it in place while the glue dries. You will need two back legs for each locust. Paint them dark brown.

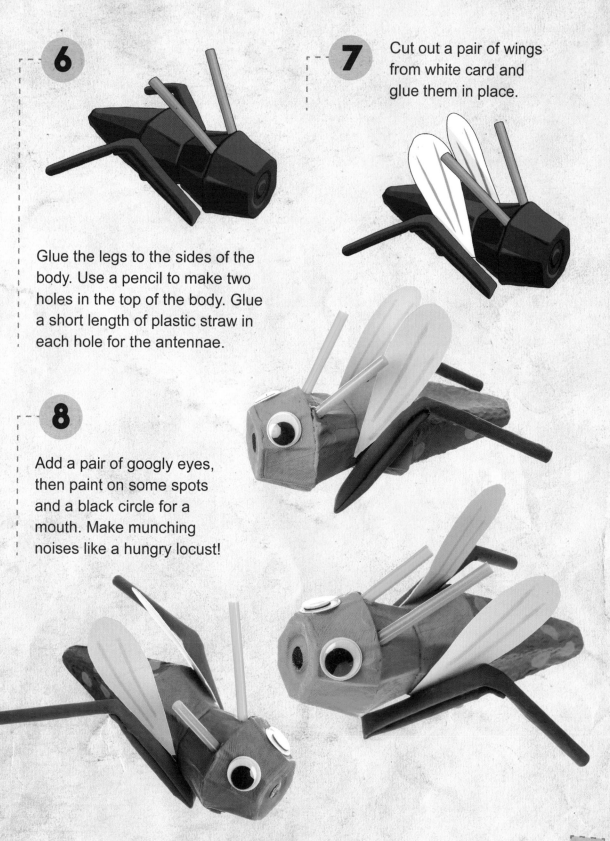

6

Glue the legs to the sides of the body. Use a pencil to make two holes in the top of the body. Glue a short length of plastic straw in each hole for the antennae.

7 Cut out a pair of wings from white card and glue them in place.

8

Add a pair of googly eyes, then paint on some spots and a black circle for a mouth. Make munching noises like a hungry locust!

Moses and the Red Sea

When wise old Moses raised his staff, God parted the Red Sea so that Moses and his people could walk across to a safe place.

You will need

One cardboard juice carton

Card

Dark red, yellow, orange and brown paint

Cord

Grey wool

One paper straw

1

Cut off the top ridge and remove the spout from the juice carton.

2

Stick some card over one side of the carton, as shown. Paint the top part skin coloured and the base dark red. Tie some cord around the middle.

3

For the cloak, cut out a piece of card – the top edge will need to wrap around three sides of the carton. Make the bottom edge slightly wider than the top. Paint it as shown.

4

Cut out a pair of sleeves and hands. Paint them as shown.

5

Glue the top of the cloak around three sides of the carton. Bend the bottom outwards. Glue on the sleeves and hands as shown.

6

Glue lengths of grey wool to the top of Moses' head for hair.

Handy Hint

Make a small hole in the bottom of your juice carton so it drains completely.

7

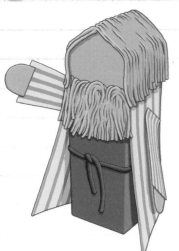

Glue shorter lengths of wool to the face to make his beard.

8

To make the nose, cut out a small triangle of card and paint it. Fold it in half and glue it to the face. Draw some eyes and cheeks. For the staff, paint a paper straw dark brown and glue it to the hand. Moses is now ready for God to part the Red Sea!

David's Slingshot

With God's help, the brave boy David used a slingshot to put an end to the scary giant, Goliath.

You will need

Thick card
Brown paint
Thick elastic
Corrugated card
One egg box

1

Cut out three Y shapes from thick card.

2

Glue the Y shapes together to make one very thick Y shape. Paint the slingshot brown.

3

Make a hole in the top ends with a pencil. Thread a piece of thick elastic through the holes and tie knots in the ends to hold it in place. Glue two strips of corrugated card around the handle.

4

Cut a bowl from the base of an egg box. Paint it dark brown.

5

Glue the egg box bowl to the middle of the elastic. The slingshot is ready!

Goliath's Shield

Make a shield like the huge one that Goliath used to protect himself from the boy David.

You will need

Thick card
Yellow and white paint
Thin card
Ten bottle tops

1

Cut out a small, medium and large circle from some thick card.

2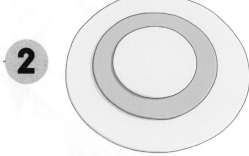

Paint the circles different shades of yellow. Glue them together, as shown.

3

To make the handle, cut a strip of thin card wider than your hand. Glue the ends to the back of the shield.

4

Glue bottle tops all around the edge and paint them yellow. Paint some white highlights on your shield to make it look like gleaming metal.

43

Hungry Lions in the Den

Daniel was made to spend a night with some hungry lions, but God made sure they didn't hurt him.

You will need (for two lions)

Two twin yoghurt pots

Yellow and pink paint

Card

Brown, red and black felt

Four googly eyes

1

Paint the outside of a twin yoghurt pot yellow.

2

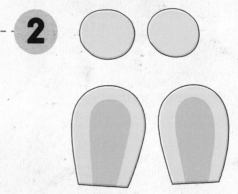

Cut out a pair of circles from some card – these are to stick the eyes on. Cut out a pair of ears. Paint them as shown.

3

Glue the ears and circles to the back of the pot. Glue a pair of googly eyes to the circles.

4

To make the mane, cut one or more long strips of brown felt – you'll need enough to go right around the pot. Cut slits along one side.

5

Turn the pot over and glue the mane around the edge.

6

Cut a tongue from some red felt and glue it inside the mouth area.

7

Cut a nose from some black felt and glue it in place. Make another hungry lion. Roaaar!

Jonah and the Big Fish

Jonah disobeyed God and tried to hide from him. When he fell into the sea, God sent a big fish to swallow Jonah and take him to dry land. Jonah didn't disobey God again.

You will need

Tapered cardboard box

Thick card

Blue, pink and white paint

Two split pins

Two googly eyes

Felt

1

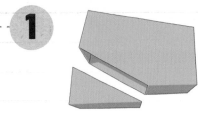

You will need a box that is narrower at one end than the other. Cut off the corner from the wide end.

2

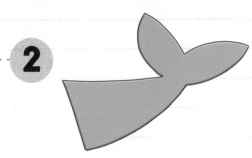

Cut out a tail from some thick card and paint it blue.

3 Paint the outside of the box blue and the inside pink.

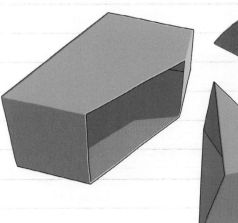

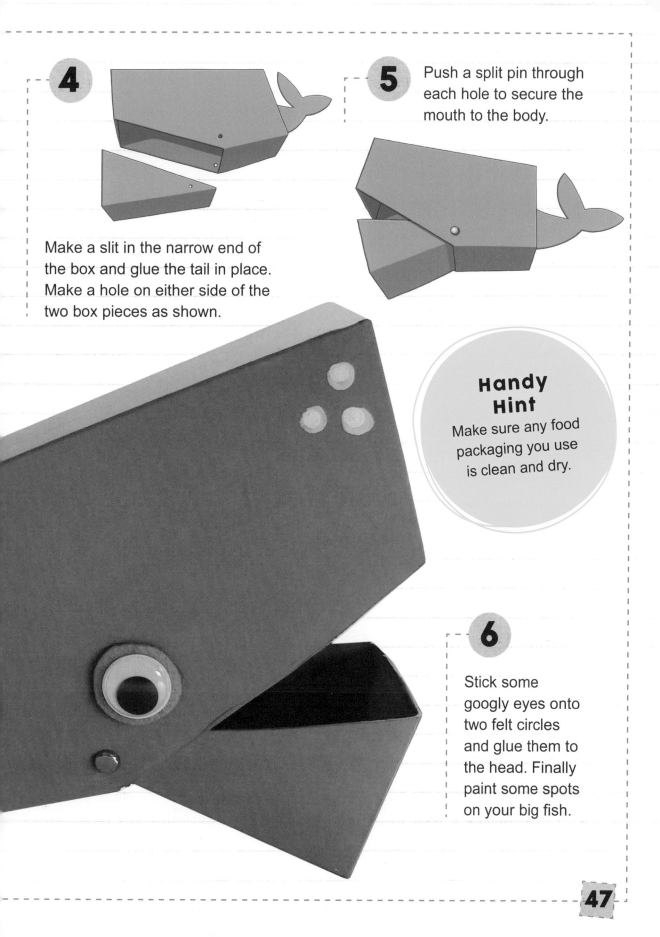

4

Make a slit in the narrow end of the box and glue the tail in place. Make a hole on either side of the two box pieces as shown.

5 Push a split pin through each hole to secure the mouth to the body.

Handy Hint
Make sure any food packaging you use is clean and dry.

6

Stick some googly eyes onto two felt circles and glue them to the head. Finally paint some spots on your big fish.

The Angel Gabriel

A shining angel named Gabriel came to Mary to tell her she was going to have a very special baby, called Jesus.

1

Paint the outside of a paper cup purple.

2

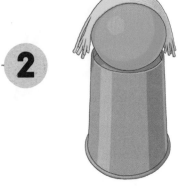

Paint a large polystyrene ball skin coloured. Glue the ball to the base of the cup. Cut some wool into equal lengths and glue the pieces to the top of the ball.

3 Twist a gold pipe cleaner into a lollipop shape for a halo.

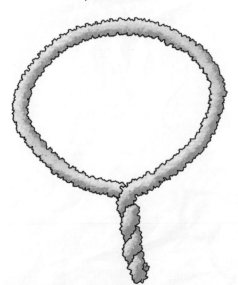

4

Make a hole in the cup behind the head and glue the halo in place. Glue the edge of a paper doily around the body.

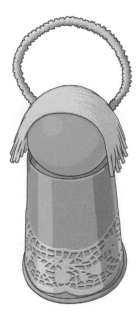

5

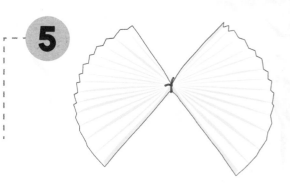

Fold a sheet of paper into a concertina shape. Squeeze the concertina in the middle and tie it with a piece of wool, then fan out both sides to make wings.

6 Glue the wings to the back of the angel.

7

Cut out a pair of sleeves and hands from thick card and paint them as shown. Glue the hands to the sleeves.

8 Glue the sleeves in place. Add a happy face. The angel has brought good news!

Mary and Joseph

This is Mary and her husband, Joseph. Joseph was a carpenter.

You will need

Two paper cups (one tall, one short)

Thick card

Red, blue, skin-coloured and brown paint

Polystyrene balls

Two fabrics

Ribbon

Brown felt

One paper straw

1

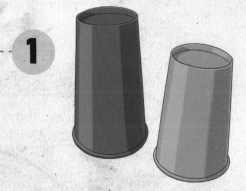

Paint a tall paper cup dark red. This will be Joseph. Paint a shorter paper cup blue for Mary.

2

Cut out two pairs of sleeves and hands from thick card. Paint them as shown.

3

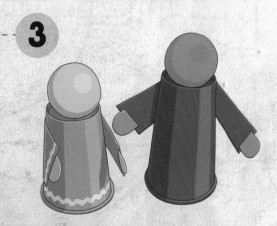

Glue on the sleeves and hands. Paint two polystyrene balls skin coloured and glue them to the base of the cups. Add some ribbon to Mary's robe.

4

Cut out a rectangle of fabric and glue it to Joseph's head.

5

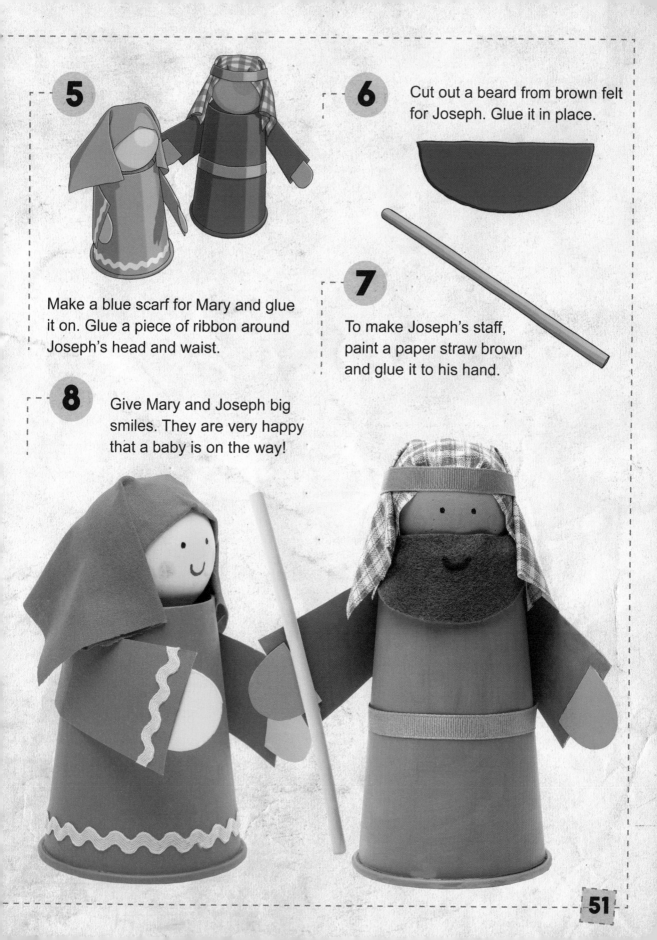

Make a blue scarf for Mary and glue it on. Glue a piece of ribbon around Joseph's head and waist.

6 Cut out a beard from brown felt for Joseph. Glue it in place.

7 To make Joseph's staff, paint a paper straw brown and glue it to his hand.

8 Give Mary and Joseph big smiles. They are very happy that a baby is on the way!

Donkey

Mary and Joseph had to travel to the town of Bethlehem. Make a sturdy little donkey like the one Mary rode.

You will need

Five cardboard tubes
Grey, white and black paint
Thick card
Black and pink felt
Two googly eyes

1

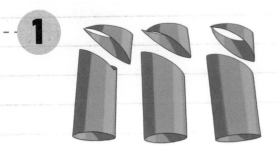

Cut the tops off three cardboard tubes at an angle as shown.

2

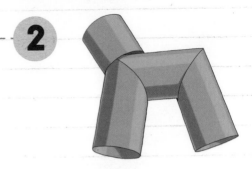

Glue two of the cut tubes to each end of a whole tube. These are the body and legs. Cut another tube in half and glue as shown for the neck.

3

To make the head, glue the remaining angled tube to the neck.

4

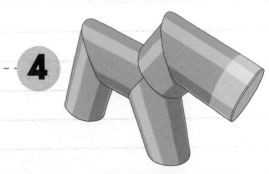

Cut out a circle of thick card and glue it to the end of the head. Paint your donkey grey. Paint a pale grey band around its nose.

5

Cut out a pair of ears from thick card and paint them grey.

6

Glue the ears in place.

7

To make the mane, cut a narrow strip of black felt and make slits all along one edge. Glue it between the ears as shown.

8

Cut a piece of card for the tail and paint it grey. Add a small piece of fringed black felt at one end. Glue the tail in place.

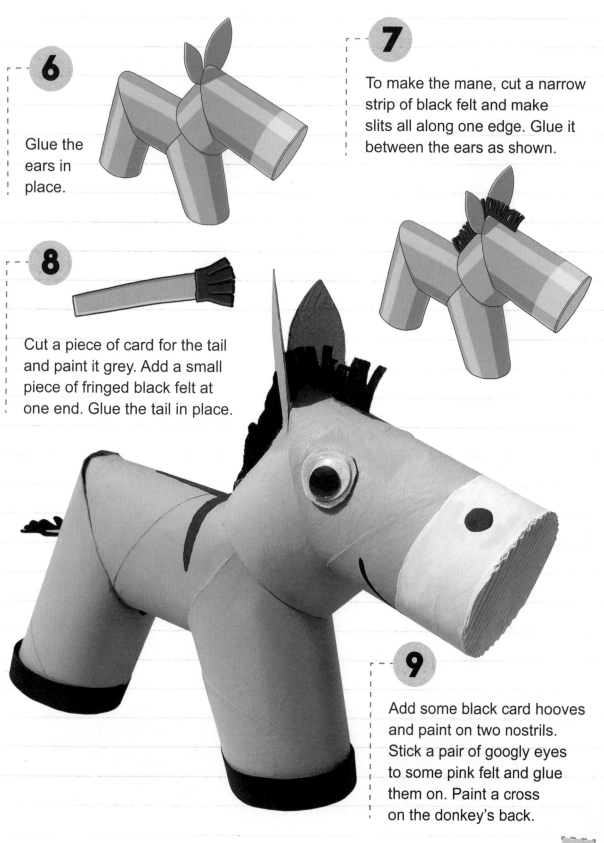

9

Add some black card hooves and paint on two nostrils. Stick a pair of googly eyes to some pink felt and glue them on. Paint a cross on the donkey's back.

Bethlehem

Make the little town of Bethlehem, with its higgledy-piggledy houses, shops and tall towers.

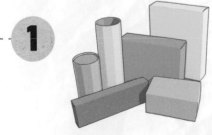

1

Paint a selection of cardboard boxes and canisters in different colours.

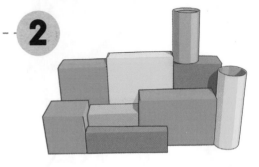

2

Glue the boxes and canisters together to make the buildings and towers of Bethlehem.

3

Paint the paper bowls and glue them to the tops of the buildings for roofs, as shown.

4

Cut out lots of windows from grey card and glue them to the buildings.

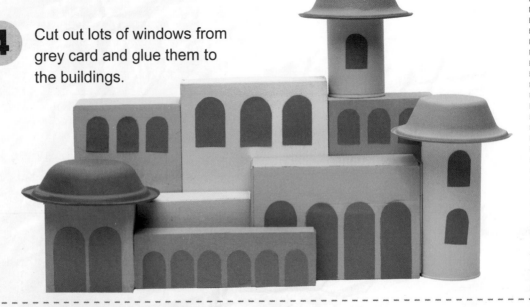

Stable

Bethlehem was so full of people when Mary and Joseph arrived that they had to sleep in a stable.

You will need

One cereal box

Light brown, dark brown and yellow paint

Corrugated card

1 Cut away one of the long, narrow sides from your box.

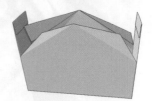

2 Cut slits half way down the four top corners. Fold in the top corners to make a roof shape, as shown.

3 Fold in the two end pieces and glue them in place.

4 Using a pencil to make a hole for your scissors, cut a double doorway. Paint the outside of the stable light brown and the inside dark brown.

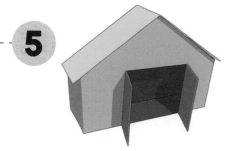

5 Glue on a piece of corrugated card for the roof. Paint it yellow.

6 Cut strips of corrugated card, paint them brown and glue them to the front. Add corrugated card to the doors. Now the stable is ready for Mary and Joseph.

Baby Jesus

Baby Jesus was born in the stable. Mary didn't have a cradle, so she laid him in a manger filled with straw.

1

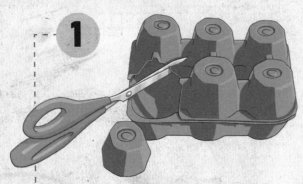

To make the manger, cut the lid off an egg box, and cut four bowls from the base of the egg box.

2

Glue the four egg box bowls to the top of the lid. Paint the manger light brown.

3

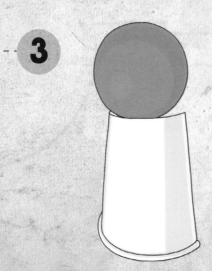

To make baby Jesus, cut a paper cup in half from top to bottom and paint it white. Paint a polystyrene ball skin coloured and glue it to the half cup.

4

Stand the manger on its feet. Cut lots of thin strips of yellow and brown paper. Scrunch them up to look like straw and place them in the manger.

5

Wrap a piece of white fabric around the cup.

6

Cut out two D-shaped pieces for hands. Paint them and fold the ends over.

7

Place baby Jesus in the manger. Glue the hands to the fabric as shown.

8

To make a halo, twist a pipe cleaner into a circle. Twist the ends together and glue the halo to the back of the head. Draw a sleepy face on baby Jesus.

Handy Hint

Always wash your brushes after use so they are ready for next time.

Shepherds

There were shepherds on the hills near Bethlehem. An angel came to tell them about baby Jesus.

1

Cut a short section from a cardboard tube and glue it to a paper cup as shown.

2

Paint the paper cup. Glue a small paper pot onto the tube and paint it skin coloured.

3

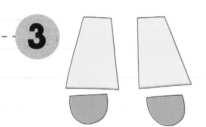

Cut out a pair of sleeves and hands from thick card and paint them.

4

Glue on the hands and sleeves. Drape some fabric over the head and attach it with an elastic band. Cover the band with cord. Tie some cord around the waist.

5

Flatten the end of a paper straw and bend it into a curve. Paint the straw brown. Glue it to the hand. Draw a smiley face. Make two more happy shepherds!

Shepherd's Lantern

The shepherds were amazed. They picked up their lanterns and went to see baby Jesus.

You will need

One round cheese box
One paper bowl
Black and white paint
One plastic bottle
One small cardboard tube
White, yellow and black card

1

Glue the lid to the base of a round cheese box. Paint the bowl and the box black.

2

Ask an adult to make a hole in a plastic bottle for your scissors, then carefully cut off the top of the bottle as shown.

3

For the candle, glue a circle of card over the end of a small cardboard tube. Paint it white. Cut a flame shape from yellow card and glue it to the top.

5

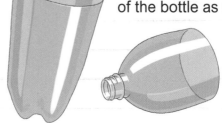

Glue the candle inside. Glue the bowl to the top. Make a ring from a strip of black card and glue it to the top. Now it's ready for the shepherds!

4

Glue the base of the bottle to the round box. Add narrow strips of black card to make a cage.

Wise Men

Later, some wise men came from a long way off to visit baby Jesus. They followed a bright star to find him.

1

You will need a box that is narrower at one end than the other. Paint it as shown.

2

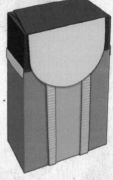

Glue some strips of shiny paper to the robe. For the face, cut out a D-shaped piece of thin card. Paint it skin coloured and glue it in place.

3

Cut out a pair of sleeves from thick card and hands from thin card. Paint them as shown, then glue the hands to the sleeves. Add some shiny paper for cuffs.

4

Cut out a beard from thick card and paint it black. Glue it to the face. Glue the sleeves to the sides and gently bend them outwards.

5

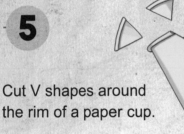

Cut V shapes around the rim of a paper cup.

6

Paint the cup yellow. Add a strip of shiny paper around the base.

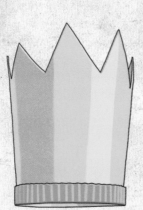

7

Glue on the crown.

8

For the nose, cut a small triangle of thin card and fold it in half. Paint it and glue it to the face.

9

Draw on the eyes, cheeks and mouth. Make two more wise men with different style beards and colourful robes.

Camel

Make this friendly camel for your wise men. You could call him HUMPhrey!

1

Cut a slit in the side of two paper bowls.

3

Cut a long, curved neck from thick card. Paint it light brown.

2

Line up the slits in the bowls and glue the bowls together. Glue a yoghurt pot on top. Paint the body light brown.

4

To make the head, cut the end off a cardboard tube. Cut a slit at one end of the long piece. Glue a circle of corrugated card over the other end. Paint the head light brown.

5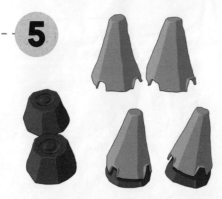

For the legs and feet, cut four bowls and four spikes from two egg boxes. Paint the spikes light brown and the egg box bowls dark brown. Glue them together as shown.

6

Glue the legs to the base of the body.

7

Slide the neck into the slot in the body and glue it in place.

8

Slide the head onto the neck and glue it in place. Cut out a pair of ears from card and paint them to match the body. Glue the ears to the camel's head.

9

Cut a tail from brown card and stick it to the body. Add a fringe of brown paper to the tail and head. Stick two googly eyes onto two circles of blue felt and glue them to the head. Finally, give your camel a cheery smile!

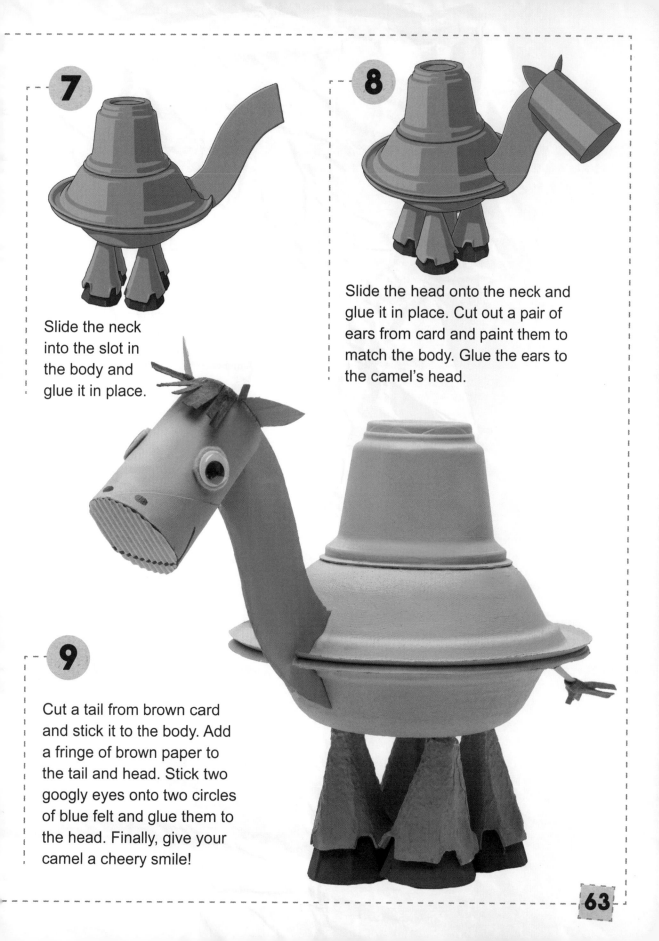

Wise Men's Gifts

The wise men brought precious gifts for baby Jesus. The gifts were fit for a king!

You will need

Three paper bowls

Paints

Seventeen bottle tops

One six- or eight-sided cardboard box

Six small boxes

One large, hinged cardboard box

Shiny corrugated card

Shiny paper

Gold

1 Glue three paper bowls together as shown.

2 Paint the casket yellow and add some stripes around the edge. Glue three bottle tops to the lid.

Frankincense

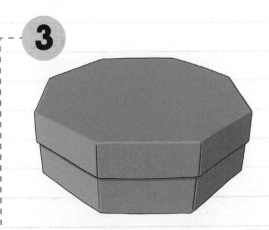

3 Paint your six- or eight-sided box purple.

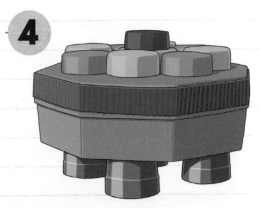

4 Glue a strip of corrugated card around the edge. Glue lots of bottle tops to the lid and four to the base for feet.

Myrrh

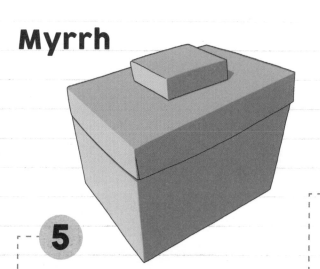

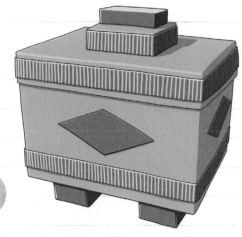

5

Glue a small box to the top of a large, hinged cardboard box.

6

Paint the casket blue. Glue a small box covered in shiny paper to the top and four to the base for feet. Decorate the casket with shiny corrugated card.

To finish

7

Add as much decoration as you want!

Handy Hint
Use glitter paint to make your three caskets look extra precious.

Jesus, our friend

The Bible tells us that Jesus is our friend, and that whatever we do, he will always love us.

You will need

One cardboard canister

Light blue and skin-coloured paint

One paper cup

White card

Blue ribbon

Brown felt

1

Paint a long cardboard canister light blue. Paint a paper cup skin coloured. Glue the cup to the top of the canister.

2

Cut out a cloak from white card. Glue some blue ribbon around the bottom edge.

3

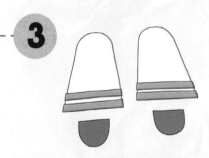

Cut out two sleeves from white card and glue on some ribbon. Cut out a pair of hands and paint them.

4

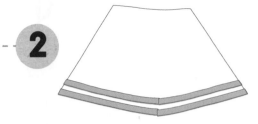

Glue the hands to the sleeves. Then glue on the cloak and sleeves as shown.

5

Cut out a beard from brown felt. Cut slits along the curved edge.

6

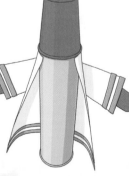

Glue the beard to the head.

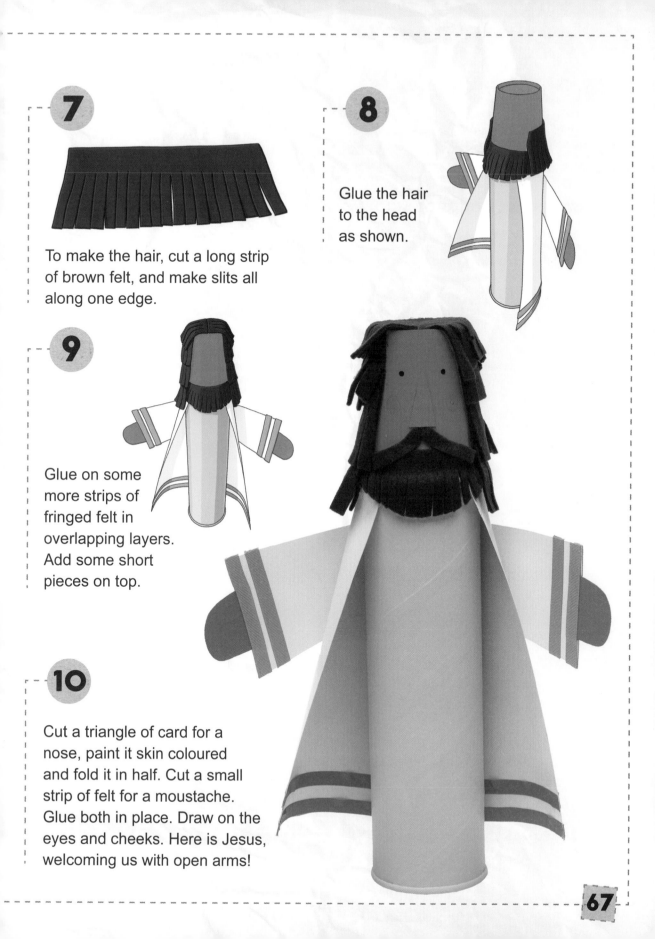

7

To make the hair, cut a long strip of brown felt, and make slits all along one edge.

8

Glue the hair to the head as shown.

9

Glue on some more strips of fringed felt in overlapping layers. Add some short pieces on top.

10

Cut a triangle of card for a nose, paint it skin coloured and fold it in half. Cut a small strip of felt for a moustache. Glue both in place. Draw on the eyes and cheeks. Here is Jesus, welcoming us with open arms!

Fishers of Men

Jesus told two fishermen: "I will make you fishers of men." The men followed Jesus and helped him to tell people about God.

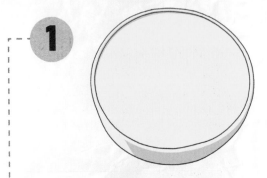

1 To make the head and body, glue the top of a round cheese box to its base.

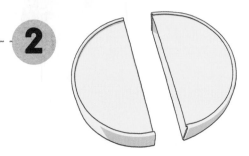

2 To make the tail, cut another cheese box in half. Glue the top to the base.

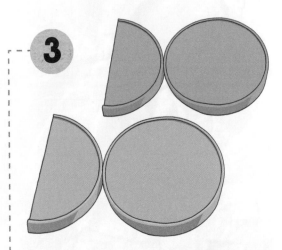

3 Glue the tail to the back of the body and paint the fish orange. Make another fish and paint it blue.

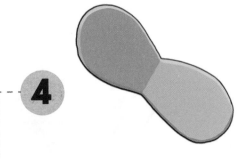

4 Fold a piece of thin card in half. Cut out a D shape, making sure the straight line of the D is along the fold. Unfold and paint the mouth to match the fish. Make another mouth.

5

Glue the fold of the mouth to the front edge of the fish as shown.

6

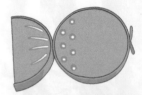

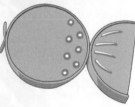

Repeat with the other fish. Paint spots on the bodies of both fish, and stripes on the tails.

7

Glue four large googly eyes to four circles of felt. Stick the eyes on either side of each fish.

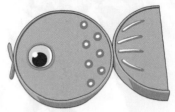

Handy Hint

PVA glue will wash off clothes with soap and water.

8

Use a stick or dowel for a fishing rod. Glue a length of ribbon to the mouth of each fish and tie it to the end of the rod. Happy fishing!

Twelve Disciples

Here are all twelve of Jesus's followers, or disciples. Make each one look a little different!

You will need

Twelve tall paper cups

Thick card

Twelve polystyrene balls

Felt

Ribbon

Paints

1

Paint a tall paper cup. Paint a band of a different colour down the front.

2

Cut out a pair of sleeves and hands from thick card and paint them.

3

Glue on the hands and sleeves as shown.

4

Paint a polystyrene ball skin coloured and glue it to the cup.

5

To make the hair, cut out a large circle of felt. Cut slits all around the edge as shown.

6

Cut out a beard shape from felt.

7

Glue the beard and hair in place. You may need to trim the fringe. Tie a piece of ribbon around the robe.

8

Draw on eyes, cheeks and a mouth. Now make eleven more disciples!

Loaves...

Jesus fed a hungry crowd of 5000 people with just five small loaves and two small fishes. And there was lots left over!

You will need
(for five loaves)

Five paper bowls
Five small paper plates
Brown paint

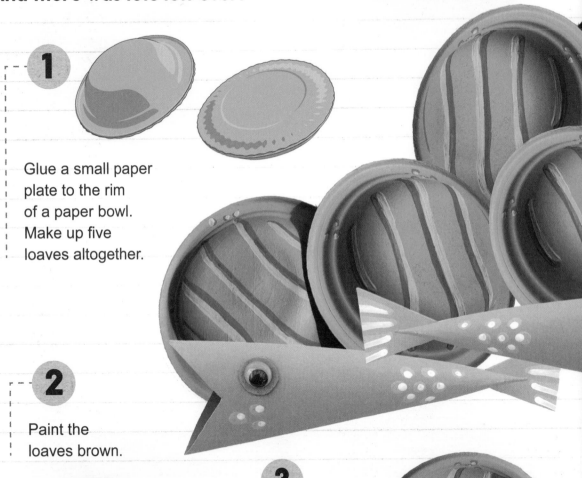

1 Glue a small paper plate to the rim of a paper bowl. Make up five loaves altogether.

2 Paint the loaves brown.

3 Add light and dark brown stripes and dots like the marks you see on a cooked loaf.

...and Fishes

You will need
(for two fishes)

Two long cardboard tubes

Blue, pink, grey and white paint

Thick card

Four googly eyes

Felt

1

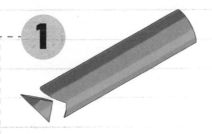

Gently flatten a long cardboard tube. To make the mouth, cut a V from one end.

2

Paint the outside blue and the inside of the mouth pink. Flatten the straight end and glue the insides together.

3

To make the tail, cut out a triangle of thick card and paint it blue. Cut a small slit in one corner, slide it onto the body and glue it in place.

4

Paint on some spots and stripes for scales and fins.

5 Stick two googly eyes to two circles of felt. Glue one on each side of the head.

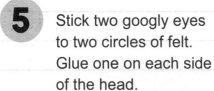

6 Make up another fish and put them with the loaves for the hungry crowd!

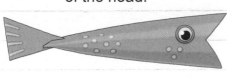
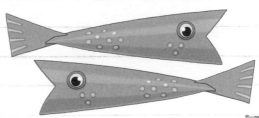

73

Lost Lamb

In one story that Jesus tells, a shepherd goes to find his little lost lamb. In the same way, if we stray from God, he will keep calling us back.

You will need

Two egg boxes

Black and white paint

One cardboard canister

One paper cup

Black card

Cotton wool balls

Two googly eyes

1

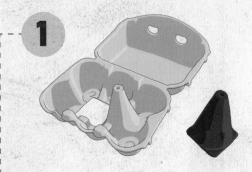

Cut four spikes from the bases of two egg boxes. Paint these black for the legs.

2

Paint a cardboard canister white. Glue on the legs as shown.

3

For the head, cut two slits in a paper cup and bend down the bit in between to make a flap. Paint the cup black.

4

Glue the flap on the cup to the front of the body.

5

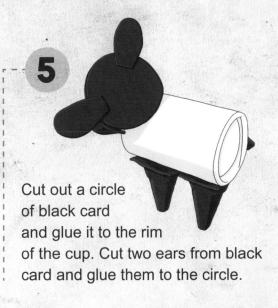

Cut out a circle of black card and glue it to the rim of the cup. Cut two ears from black card and glue them to the circle.

6

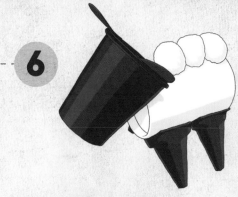

Now make your little lamb fluffy! Starting at the top, glue a row of cotton wool balls to the body.

7

Keep glueing cotton wool balls to the body until it is completely covered.

Handy Hint

Don't press the cotton wool balls too hard or they will lose their shape.

8

Add two googly eyes. Baaa! Your cute little lamb is ready to roam.

BAAA

Palm Tree and Leaves

When Jesus came to Jerusalem, people cheered and laid palm leaves down like a carpet.

You will need

Six long cardboard tubes

Dark green, light green and brown paint

Five lolly sticks

Corrugated card

1

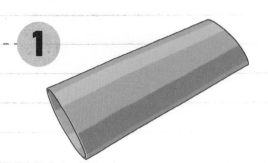

Gently flatten a long cardboard tube.

2

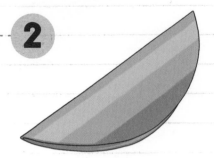

Cut off one side to leave a curved piece.

3

Cut slits all along the curved edges.

4

Open the piece out to make a leaf. Paint it dark green on top and light green underneath.

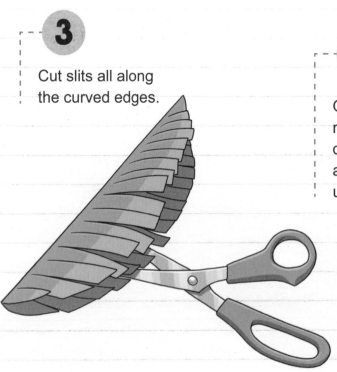

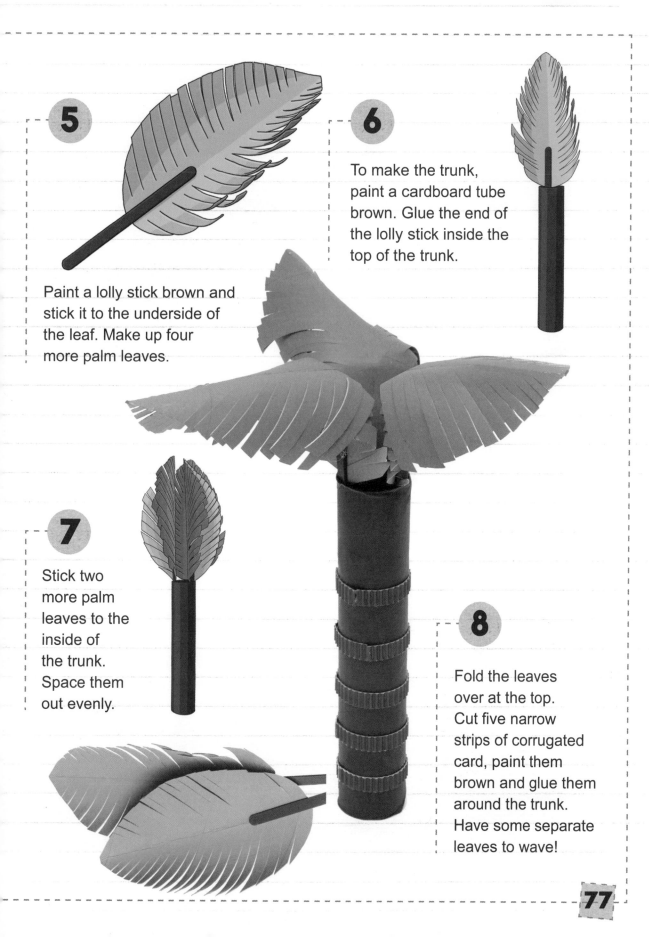

5

Paint a lolly stick brown and stick it to the underside of the leaf. Make up four more palm leaves.

6

To make the trunk, paint a cardboard tube brown. Glue the end of the lolly stick inside the top of the trunk.

7

Stick two more palm leaves to the inside of the trunk. Space them out evenly.

8

Fold the leaves over at the top. Cut five narrow strips of corrugated card, paint them brown and glue them around the trunk. Have some separate leaves to wave!

Cross with Flowers

When we see a cross, we think of Jesus and his great love for us. Make this beautiful cross.

1

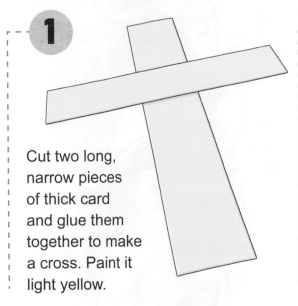

Cut two long, narrow pieces of thick card and glue them together to make a cross. Paint it light yellow.

2

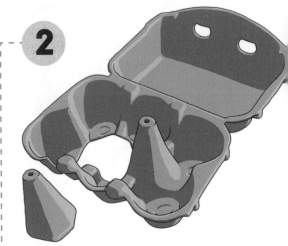

Cut all sixteen spikes from the bases of eight egg boxes.

3

Cut notches in six of the spikes to make flower buds. Paint the buds white.

4

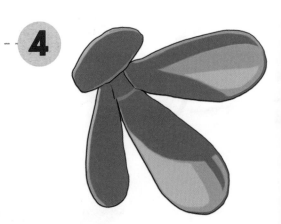

Cut ten of the spikes as shown to make four open petals joined at the base.

5

Paint the petals pink and purple. Glue two lots of petals together to make a flower. Repeat four times to make five flowers altogether.

6

Cut out lots of leaf shapes from the tops of your egg boxes and paint them green.

7

Glue the leaves, flower buds and flowers to the middle of the cross. Add some balls of yellow tissue paper to the middle of the flowers.

Handy Hint
Use old yoghurt pots to mix lots of shades of pink and purple paint.

Quarto is the authority on a wide range of topics.
Quarto educates, entertains and enriches the lives of
our readers—enthusiasts and lovers of hands-on living.
www.quartoknows.com

Design and Editorial: Starry Dog Books Ltd
Photography: Michael Wicks
Illustration: Tom Connell

First published in the UK in 2017
by QED Publishing
Part of The Quarto Group
The Old Brewery, 6 Blundell Street
London, N7 9BH

A catalogue record for this book is available from the British Library.

ISBN 978 1 78493 767 6

Printed in China